Contents

Special Features

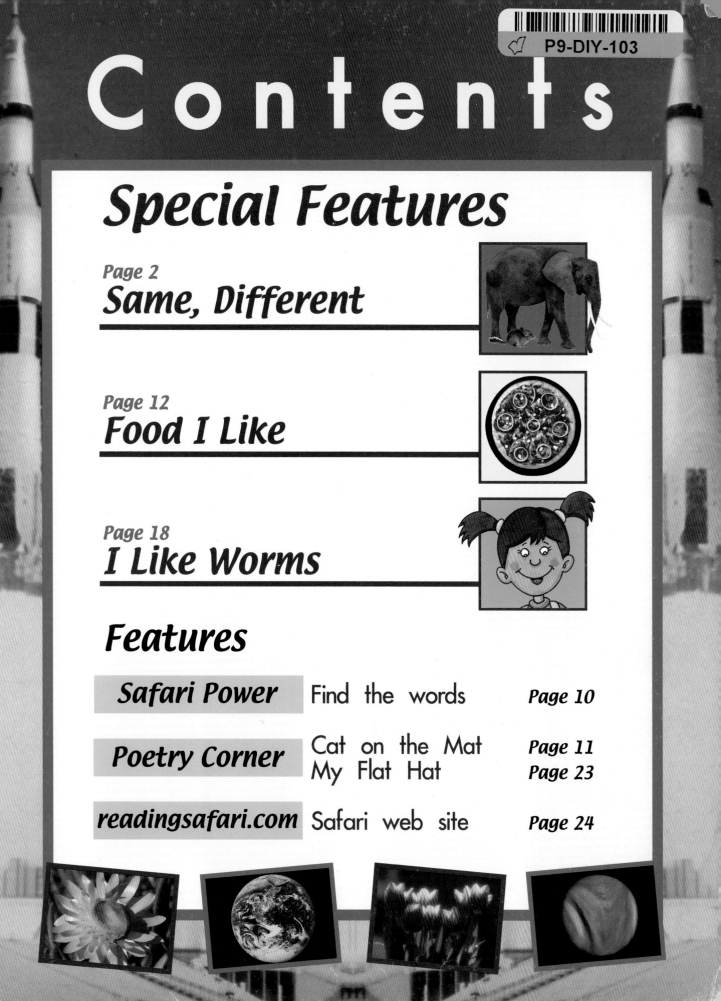

Features

P9-DIY-103

Same, Different

Written by Josephine Selwyn

Same

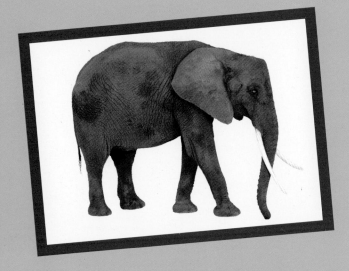 

Different

Same

Different

4

Same

Different

Same

Different

6

Same

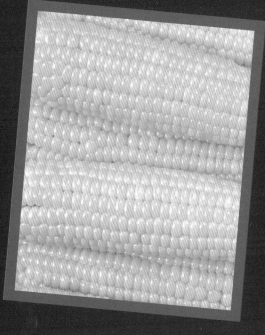 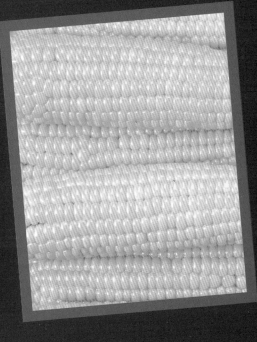

Different

Same

Different

Same

Different

Safari
WORD POWER

Aa

Bb

Cc

Dd

Ee

Ff

Gg

Hh

Ii

Jj Kk Ll Mm Nn Oo Pp Qq

Zz

Yy

Xx

Ww

Vv

Uu

Tt

Ss

Rr

I   dog cat girl

like

am

boy

Find –
I, am, like, dog,
cat, boy, girl

Cat on the Mat

Written by Krystal Diaz
Illustrated by Trevor Pye

A fat cat,
A fat rat.
Run, run, run,
Around the mat!

bat
cat
fat
flat
hat
mat
pat
rat
sat
bat
cat
fat
flat
hat
mat
pat
rat
sat

Food I Like

Written by Simone Santo
Illustrated by Bruce Potter

I like rice.

I like pasta.

I like sushi.

I like pizza.

I like nachos.

I like burgers.

I Like Worms

Written by Michele Ashley
Illlustrated by Kelvin Hawley

Bird

Boy

Cat

Girl

Worm

Boy
I like dogs.

Cat
I do not like dogs.

Girl

I like cats.

Bird

I do not like cats.

 **Boy**
I like birds.

Worm

I do not like birds.

Girl

I like worms.

Boy

I do not like worms.

My Flat Hat

Written by Monique Martin

Illustrated by Kelvin Hawley

I have a hat.
A big blue hat.
Oh no! Oh no!
My hat is flat!

readingsafari.com

Check out these Safari magazines, too!

Have your say -

e-mail your Safari Tour Guide at
tourguide@readingsafari.com

Safari Tour Guide,   🌵 40

I wrote a story about food I like.

Do you want me to send it to you?

Jarod Gordon (5)

Safari Superstar

Name – Xavier

Birthday – November 18

Find out more about this Safari Superstar at
http://www.readingsafari.com